C.2

PEAVINE SCHOOL

SOUNDS OF LANGUAGE

SOUNDS LANGUAGE readers

Sounds of Children
   at Play on the Hill
Sounds Around the Mountain
Sounds of an Owly Night
Sounds of Home
Sounds of Numbers
Sounds Around the Clock
Sounds of a Powwow
Sounds of Laughter

D1472760

pictures by Ed Renfro

SOUNDS
of Laughter

By Bill Martin Jr
with Peggy Brogan and
John Archambault

One DLM Park • Allen, Texas 75002

ACKNOWLEDGMENTS

Acknowledgment is made to Betty Jean Mitchell for permission to use her character Noodles © 1981.

Thanks to Linda Ross and Carol Misiaszek for their editorial and production assistance.

Every effort has been made to locate and secure permissions from the copyright holders for the stories used in this book. The publishers will be grateful if any omissions or errors are brought to their attention, so that they may be corrected.

Copyright © 1990 by DLM
All rights reserved. No part of this material shall be reproduced or transmitted in any form or by any means, electronic or mechanical, including photocopying, or by any information or retrieval system, without written permission from the publisher.
ISBN 1-55924-371-6. Printed in the U.S.A.

1 2 3 4 5 6 7 8 9   96 95 94 93 92 91 90

Cover art by Kelly Oechsli.

"The River Is a Piece of Sky" from THE REASON FOR THE PELICAN by John Ciardi. Copyright © 1959 by John Ciardi. Copyright renewed. Reprinted by permission of Judith H. Ciardi.

"Keep a Poem in Your Pocket" excerpted from "Keep a Poem in Your Pocket" from SOMETHING SPECIAL by Beatrice Schenk de Regniers. © 1958, 1986 by Beatrice Schenk de Regniers. Reprinted by permission of the author.

"Out in the Rain" from JUST AROUND THE CORNER by Leland B. Jacobs. Copyright © 1964 by Leland B. Jacobs. Reprinted by permission of Henry Holt and Company, Inc.

"Listen, Listen" from THE AMERICAN MOTHER GOOSE by Ray Wood. (J. B. Lippincott), Copyright © 1940, renewed 1968 by Ray Wood. Reprinted by permission of Harper & Row, Publishers, Inc.

"How Many Miles to Old Norfolk" (the text and illustrations) from FATHER FOX'S PENNY-RHYMES by Clyde Watson, illustrated by Wendy Watson. (Crowell) Text Copyright © 1971 by Clyde Watson. Illustrations Copyright © 1971 by Wendy Watson. Reprinted by permission of Harper & Row, Publishers, Inc.

"Jenny the Juvenile Juggler" by Dennis Lee. © Dennis Lee. Reprinted by permission of McKnight Gosewich Associates Agency Inc.

"The Tiger, the Brâhman, and the Jackal" from TALES OF THE PUNJAB by Flora Annie Steele was originally published by Macmillan Press Ltd., Basingstoke, Hampshire.

"Joey Kangaroo" by Patricia K. Miller and Iran L. Seligman is used by permission of Iran L. Seligman.

CONTENTS

Listen, Listen   10
    an old jingle
    picture by Ed Renfro

I Like Kids   12
    a poem by Noodles

The Funny Old Woman
and The Funny Old Man   14
    by Martha Barber
    pictures by Ed Renfro

How Many Blackbirds   38
    an old rhyme
    drawings by Kelly Oechsli

The Old Woman and Her Pig   40
    an old, old story
    pictures adapted by Aldren Watson
    from old drawings by Frederick Richardson

Susie Moriar 54
    an old jingle
    picture by Ed Renfro

The Three Billy-Goats Gruff 56
    a Norwegian folktale
    woodcuts by Susan Blair

Wow Pow 68
    a word puzzle
    design by Eric Carle

Grasshoppers Three 70
    an old song
    picture by Carole Kofod Butterfield

Gathering Gold 72
    by Katherine Edelman
    picture by Tom Huffman

The Star-Spangled Banner 74
    by Francis Scott Key
    drawing by Don Mackay

Sleeping Out 76
    by Bill Martin Jr
    paintings by Symeon Shimin

Old Lucy Lindy and the Pies 84
    by Leland B. Jacobs
    pictures by Ed Renfro

A Nest of Robins 92
    by Bill Martin Jr
    painting by Bernard Martin

I Love the Mountains 94
    an old camp song
    picture by Val Thelin

Little Red-Cap 96
    by the Brothers Grimm
    woodcuts by Susan Blair

Out In the Rain 114
by Leland B. Jacobs
picture by Ed Renfro

Joey Kangaroo 116
by Patricia K. Miller and Iran L. Seligman
pictures by Ed Renfro

Monday's Child 130
an old rhyme adapted by Bill Martin Jr
pictures by Sonia O. Lisker

How Many Miles to Old Norfolk 138
a rhyme by Clyde Watson
pictures by Wendy Watson

The River Is a Piece of Sky 140
by John Ciardi
picture by Ed Young

Knots on a Counting Rope 142
by Bill Martin Jr
pictures by Joe Smith

Jenny the Juvenile Juggler 160
by Dennis Lee
pictures by Peter Lippman

The Tiger, the Brâhman, and
the Jackal 168
a folktale of India
pictures by Mamoru Funai

Keep a Poem in Your Pocket 192
by Beatrice Schenk de Regniers
drawing by Charles Brey

SOUNDS OF LAUGHTER

picture by Ed Renfro

Listen, Listen

Listen, listen and you shall hear
How the old cow died with a bug in her ear.
The bug flew out,
The wind blew in,
The old cow's up and gone again.

an old jingle

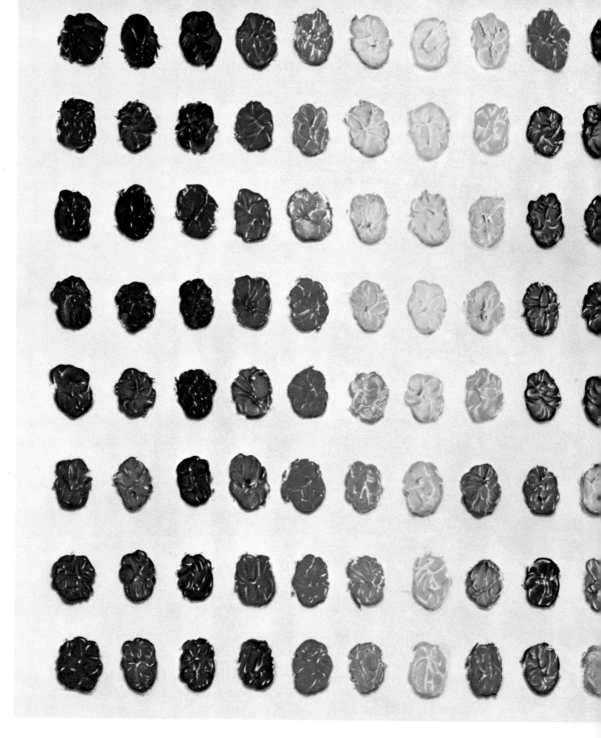

The children of the world
are a gallery of colors.

artwork courtesy of Winsor & Newton

I like kids,
I like them lots,
I like them cold,
I like them hots,
I like them quiet,
I like them noisy,
I like them girlsy,
I like them boysy.

The Funny Old Man

by Martha Barber

A funny old man and a funny old woman
  sat by the fire one night.
"Funny old man," the old woman said,
  "I don't know what to do.
When I went to the barn to milk the cow,
  the funny old cow wouldn't moo."

and the Funny Old Woman

pictures by Ed Renfro

The funny old man scratched his head.
"I know what to do," he said.
"Take her to town to see Doctor Brown,
and bring her home in the morning.
That's what you do when the cow won't moo."

"But she's out in the woodshed lying down.
How will you take the cow to town
and bring her back in the morning?"

"If she can't walk," said the funny old man,
"I'll push her in the wheelbarrow if I can,
and walk her home in the morning."

"But the goat's asleep in the wheelbarrow.
Where shall I put the goat?"

"Put the goat on top of the garden gate.
   The goat can sleep there very late
      till the cow comes home in the morning."

"But the rooster is roosting on the garden gate.
   Where shall I put the rooster?"

"Put the rooster in the butter churn,
    so tight that he can't twist or turn
    till the cow comes home in the morning."

"But my nice fresh butter is in the churn.
    Where shall I put the butter?"

21

"Put the butter on a string in the garden pool,
   and it will keep there fresh and cool
   till the cow comes home in the morning."

"But the fish is in the garden pool.
  Where shall I put the fish?"

"Put the fish in some water in the old washtub,
   so he can give his fins a scrub
   till the cow comes home in the morning."

"But the cat's asleep in the old washtub.
  Where shall I put the cat?"

"Put the cat in the fruit bowl. Then she'll dream
of nice red strawberries laced with cream
till the cow comes home in the morning."

"But the figs are in the fruit bowl.
Where shall I put the figs?"

"Put the figs in the barn on a pile of wheat.
They'll keep quite firm and fresh and sweet
till the cow comes home in the morning."

"But the pig is sleeping on the pile of wheat.
What shall I do with the pig?"

"Put the pig on a pillow in the feather bed,
to snooze and snore," the old man said,
"till the cow comes home in the morning."

"No," said the woman. "I sleep on the bed.
Where shall I lay my funny old head?"

The old man cried, "Put the pig in the bed!
And you can stand on your funny old head
   till the cow comes home in the morning."

So the funny old woman flipped up on her head.
"It's really quite cozy here," she said,
   "till the cow comes home in the morning."

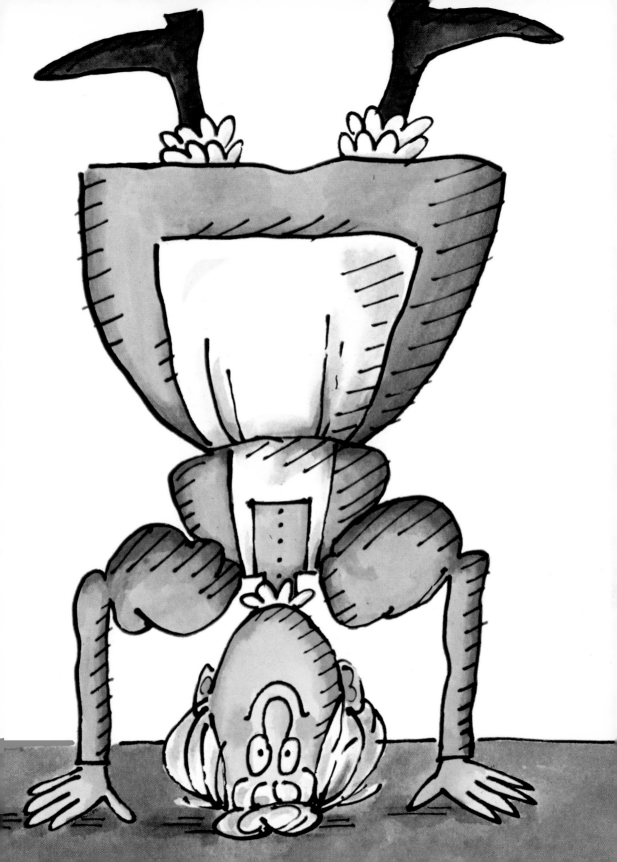

Then late that night the funny old man
pushed the funny old cow to town.

They rolled in the light of the bright, full moon
till they found old Doctor Brown.

The doctor thumped on the old cow's hide,
he tickled her tonsils and looked inside.
"Old man," said the doctor, "your cow's not sick.
She merely wanted the ride!"

The old man cried, "Can this be true?"
The cow replied with a happy "Moo."

And they both went home in the morning.

How Many Blackbirds in a tree?

Count, and you'll your fortune see

1 You'll be sorry,

2 You'll be glad,

3 You'll meet a girl,

4 You'll meet a lad.

5 You'll win silver,

6 You'll win gold,

7 You'll hear a secret that's never been told.

an old rhyme, drawings by Kelly Oechsli

The Old Woman and Her Pig

an old, old story, pictures adapted by Aldren Watson,
from old drawings by Frederick Richardson

An Old Woman found a sixpence.
She said,

"What shall I do with this sixpence?
I will buy a pig."

So she bought a pig.

On the way home they came to a stile.

The Old Woman said,

  "Pig, pig, jump over the stile."

The pig said,

  "I will not jump over the stile."

The Old Woman went on

till she met a dog.

She said,

"Dog, dog, bite pig!

Pig will not jump over the stile,

and I shall not get home to-night."

The dog said,

"No, I will not bite pig."

The Old Woman went on
    till she met a stick.
She said,
    "Stick, stick, beat dog!
    Dog will not bite pig.
    Pig will not jump over the stile,
    and I shall not get home to-night."
The stick said,
    "No, I will not beat dog."

The Old Woman went on
   till she met a fire.
She said,
   "Fire, fire, burn stick!
   Stick will not beat dog.
   Dog will not bite pig.
   Pig will not jump over the stile,
   and I shall not get home to-night."
The fire said,
   "No, I will not burn stick."

44

The Old Woman went on
　till she met some water.
She said,
　"Water, water, quench fire!
　　Fire will not burn stick.
　　Stick will not beat dog.
　　Dog will not bite pig.
　　Pig will not jump over the stile,
　　and I shall not get home to-night."
The water said,
　"No, I will not quench fire."

The Old Woman went on

    till she met an ox.

She said,

    "Ox, ox, drink water!

      Water will not quench fire.

      Fire will not burn stick.

      Stick will not beat dog.

      Dog will not bite pig.

      Pig will not jump over the stile,

      and I shall not get home to-night."

The ox said,

    "No, I will not drink water."

The Old Woman went on
   till she met a butcher.
She said,
   "Butcher, butcher, kill ox!
   Ox will not drink water.
   Water will not quench fire.
   Fire will not burn stick.
   Stick will not beat dog.
   Dog will not bite pig.
   Pig will not jump over the stile,
   and I shall not get home to-night."
The butcher said,
   "No, I will not kill ox."

The Old Woman went on
  till she met a rope.
She said,
  "Rope, rope, hang butcher!
   Butcher will not kill ox.
   Ox will not drink water.
   Water will not quench fire.
   Fire will not burn stick.
   Stick will not beat dog.
   Dog will not bite pig.
   Pig will not jump over the stile,
   and I shall not get home to-night."
The rope said,
  "No, I will not hang butcher."

The Old Woman went on
  till she met a rat.
She said, "Rat, rat, gnaw rope!
  Rope will not hang butcher.
  Butcher will not kill ox.
  Ox will not drink water.
  Water will not quench fire.
  Fire will not burn stick.
  Stick will not beat dog.
  Dog will not bite pig.
  Pig will not jump over the stile,
  and I shall not get home to-night."
The rat said, "Get me some cheese.
  Then I will gnaw the rope."

The Old Woman got some cheese.

She gave it to the rat.

Then the rat

   began to gnaw the rope.

The rope began

   to hang the butcher.

The butcher began

   to kill the ox.

The ox began to drink the water.

The water began to quench the fire.

The fire began to burn the stick.

The stick began to beat the dog.

The dog began to bite the pig.

The pig jumped over the stile,
and the Old Woman
got home that night.

an old jingle
picture by Ed Renfro

Susie Moriar

This is the story
Of Susie Moriar.
It started one night
As she sat by the fire.

The fire was so hot,
Susie jumped in a pot.
The pot was so black,
Susie dropped in a crack.

The crack was so narrow,
Susie climbed on a wheelbarrow.
The wheelbarrow was so low,
Susie fell in the snow.

The snow was so white,
Susie stayed there all night.
The night was so long,
Susie sang a song.

The song was so sweet,
Susie ran down the street. The street was so clean, Susie picked up a bean.

The bean was so hard, Susie dropped it in lard. The lard was so greasy, Susie nearly jumped fleecy.

And when she came down,

She ran through the town.

The town was so big,

Susie jumped on a pig.

The pig jumped so high,

He touched the sky—

He touched the sky

And he couldn't jump higher,

But, oh,

What a ride had Susie Moriar.

The Three Billy-Goats Gruff

a Norwegian folktale
woodcuts by Susan Blair

Once on a time there were three billy-goats,
who were to go up to the hillside
to make themselves fat,
and the name of all three was "Gruff."

On the way up was a bridge;
and under the bridge lived a great ugly Troll
with eyes as big as saucers,
and a nose as long as a poker.

So first of all
    came the youngest billy-goat Gruff
    to cross the bridge.

"Trip, trap! trip, trap!" went the bridge.

"WHO'S THAT tripping over my bridge?"
    roared the Troll.

"Oh, it is only I,
    the tiniest billy-goat Gruff;
    and I'm going up to the hillside
    to make myself fat,"
    said the billy-goat.

"Now, I'm coming to gobble you up," said the Troll.

"Oh no! pray don't take me.
  I'm too little, that I am," said the billy-goat;
  "wait a bit till the second billy-goat Gruff comes,
    he's much bigger."

"Well, be off with you!" said the Troll.

A little while after
   came the second billy-goat Gruff
   to cross the bridge.

"Trip, Trap! Trip, Trap! Trip, Trap!"
   went the bridge.

"WHO'S THAT tripping over my bridge?"
   roared the Troll.

"Oh, it's the second billy-goat Gruff,
   and I'm going up to the hillside
   to make myself fat,"
   said the billy-goat,
   who hadn't such a small voice.

"Now, I'm coming to gobble you up,"
    said the Troll.

"Oh no! don't take me;
    wait a little till the big billy-goat Gruff comes,
    he's much bigger."

"Very well, be off with you!"
    said the Troll.

But just then up came the big billy-goat Gruff.

"TRIP, TRAP! TRIP, TRAP!"
> went the bridge, for the billy-goat was so heavy
> that the bridge creaked and groaned under him.

"WHO'S THAT tripping over my bridge?"
> roared the Troll.

"IT'S I! THE BIG BILLY-GOAT GRUFF,"
> said the billy-goat
> who had an ugly hoarse voice of his own.

"Now, I'm coming to gobble you up,"
> roared the Troll.

"Well, come along! I've got two spears,
    And I'll poke your eyeballs out at your ears;
    I've got besides two curling-stones,
    And I'll crush you to bits, body and bones."

That was what the big billy-goat said;
    and so he flew at the Troll
    and poked his eyes out with his horns, and
    crushed him to bits, body and bones,
    and tossed him out into the burn,
    and after that he went up to the hillside.

There the billy-goats got so fat
    they were scarce able to walk home again;
    and if the fat hasn't fallen off them,
    why, they're still fat; and so:

Snip,

   snap,

      snout,

         This tale's told out.

soda
pop

gum
drops

Endow me now
   with my favorite chow!
Wow! Pow!
   Like hot dogs, crackerjacks,
      ice cream
      and bubble gum!

a brown

OW

how nice!

NOW

OW

pop-corn

lolli-pops

but I like spinach!

design by Eric Carle

69

Grasshoppers Three

a-fiddling went,
Hey, ho, never be still,
They had no money to pay the rent
But all day long with their elbows bent

They fiddled a tune called
"Riddleby-Riddleby,"
Fiddled
a
tune
called,
"Riddleby Rill."

an old song
illustration by Carole Kofod Butterfield

"GATHERING GOLD" BY KATHERINE EDELMAN, PAINTING BY TOM HUFFMAN

I walked through autumn woods today,
I cupped my hands along the way.
The trees shook down their coins of gold,
More than my two hands could hold.

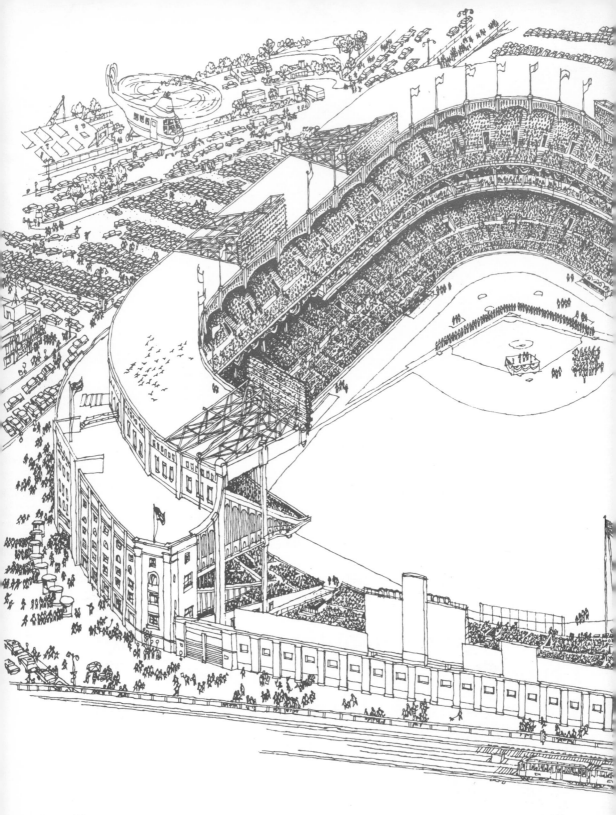

The Star-Spangled Banner

A song with words by Francis Scott Key and music by John Stafford Smith, line drawing by Don Mackay

O say! can you see,
by the dawn's early light,
What so proudly we hail'd
at the twilight's last gleaming?
Whose broad stripes
and bright stars,
thro' the perilous fight,
O'er the ramparts we watch'd,
were so gallantly streaming?
And the rocket's red glare,
the bombs bursting in air,
Gave proof thro' the night
that our flag was still there.
O say, does that
Star-Spangled Banner yet wave

O ★ er the land of the free
and the home of the brave?

75

Sleeping Out

by Bill Martin Jr

paintings by Symeon Shimin

I can sleep out tonight,
Mom said,

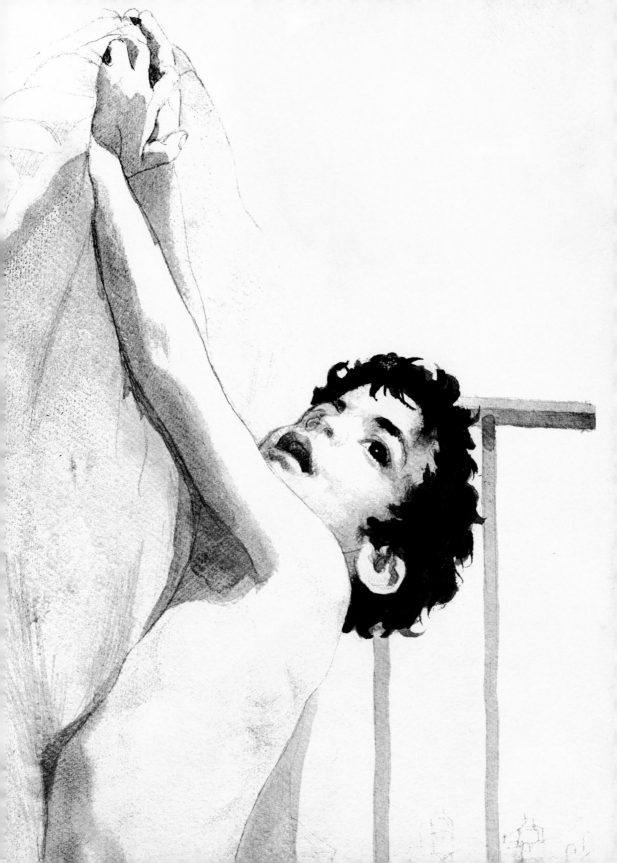

Long before dark
I'm ready for bed,

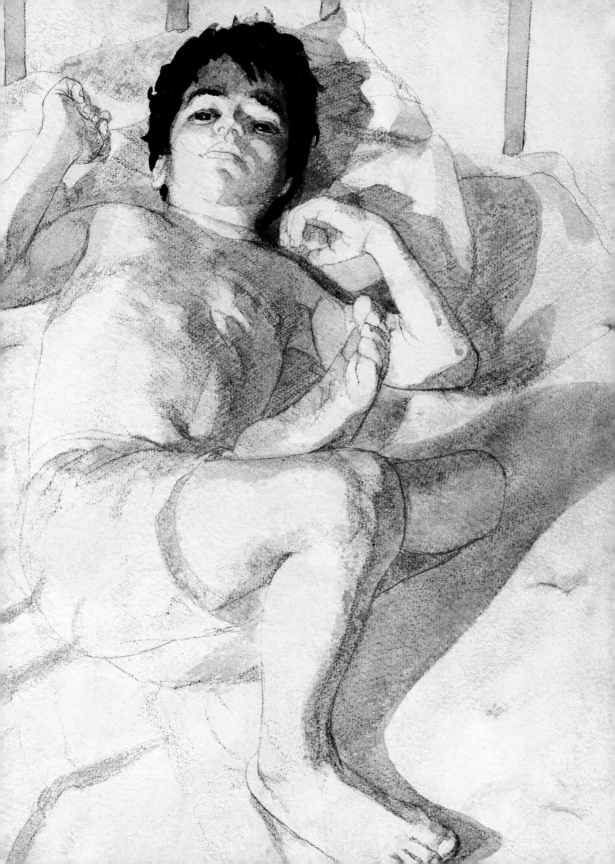

The summer night
Is fairy light

That stays in my head
Till morning.

Old Lucy Lindy and the Pies

by Leland B. Jacobs
pictures by Ed Renfro

Old Lucy Lindy liked to bake.
She liked to bake pies.
She liked to bake cakes.

She baked many kinds of cakes:
    dark cakes,
    light cakes,
    layer cakes, and
    white cakes.

She had no trouble with her cakes.
She knew her light cakes from her
    dark cakes.
She knew her layer cakes.

Old Lucy baked many kinds of pies:
    apple pies,
    blueberry pies,
    mince pies, and
    cherry pies.

But she had trouble with her pies.
They were all covered with crust.
She could not tell one pie from another.

After it was baked, was it a mince pie?

Or was it an apple pie?

"My, what trouble!"

she said to herself.

One morning Old Lucy decided to bake.

She decided to bake five pies:

2 apple pies

1 blueberry pie

2 mince pies.

As she made the crust she had an idea.

"Now I'll know one pie from another,"

she said to herself.

She took a knife.

She put two letters in the crust.

In the mince pies she put I.M.

"That means IS MINCE,"

she said to herself.

She put two letters in the crust

of the other pies.

The letters were I.M.

"That means ISN'T MINCE,"

she said to herself.

Old Lucy baked her 2 apple pies.
She put them out on the right
    of the shelf.
She baked her 1 blueberry pie.
She put it on the right
    of the kitchen shelf.
She baked her 2 mince pies.
She put them out on the left
    of the shelf.

Old Lucy Lindy looked at her pies.
She looked left, at her mince pies.
    "I.M. means IS MINCE," she said.
She looked right, at her apple
    and blueberry pies.

    "I.M.," she said, "ISN'T MINCE."
    "My, my!" she said.
    "That's a good idea! Now I know
      which pie is which."

The Robin

The American robin is familiar
to nearly everyone
in the United States and Canada.
This friendly bird is seen
in gardens and meadows everywhere,
particularly those
that lie near trees and shrubs
and gentle woodlands.
The robin is an early riser,
awakening at the first sign of dawn.
It greets the day with a morning song
that lasts about 30 minutes,
"Cheer up! Cheer up! Cheer, cheer up!"
Then it stops singing
and goes about the necessary task
of finding worms and bugs and seeds
for itself and its babies to eat.

by Bill Martin Jr
painting by Bernard Martin

I Love the Mountains,

I love the rolling hills,

I love the flowers,

I love the daffodils,

I love the fireside

when all the lights are low,

Boom - dee - ah - dah,

Boom - dee - ah - dah,

Boom.

an old camp song
picture by Val Thelin

Little Red-Cap

by the Brothers Grimm
translated by Werner Linz
woodcuts by Susan Blair

Once upon a time
there was a sweet little maiden
who was loved by everyone who knew her.
But her grandmother loved her most of all,
and would give her anything.

One day her grandmother
gave her a little cap of red velvet,
which looked so pretty on her
that she wore it all the time.
And so she was called "Little Red-Cap."

One day her mother said to her,
"Come, Little Red-Cap.
Here is a piece of cake and a bottle of milk.
Take these to Grandmother.
She is sick and weak
and they will comfort her.
Now, be a good girl
and remember to greet her for me.
Walk carefully along the path
and be sure not to go into the forest."

Little Red-Cap promised her mother
that she would be careful,
and that she would remember everything
she had been told.

Then she started out.

Now, her grandmother
lived far out in the forest,
half a league from the village,
and as soon as Little Red-Cap
entered the forest,
she met the wolf.
Little Red-Cap did not know
what a wicked animal he was,
and so she was not afraid of him.

"Good-day, Little Red-Cap,"
  said the wolf.

"Thank you kindly, Wolf,"
  said Little Red-Cap.

"Where are you going so early, Little Red-Cap?"

"To Grandmother's house."

"And what are you carrying in your basket?"

"Cake and milk for Grandmother.
  She is sick and weak,
    and this will make her stronger."

"And where
does your Grandmother live,
Little Red-Cap?"

"Another quarter of a league through the forest.
Her house stands under the big oak trees.
You must know where it is."

The wolf thought,
"This will be a tender mouthful.
Now, how do I go about getting it?"

The wolf walked along with her a little way,
and then he said,
"Little Red-Cap, do you not see the flowers?
Do you not hear how sweetly the birds are singing?
You walk along as if you were going to school
back in that little village,
while out here in the forest it is so gay!"

Little Red-Cap stopped and looked around.
She saw how beautifully
the sun's rays broke through the trees
and shone on the flowers.

She thought, "Ah!
If I should bring a bouquet to Grandmother,
how she would like that!
It is still early,
and there is enough time to get there."

And she darted off into the forest
to look for flowers.
But as soon as she had picked one,
she was sure she saw an even prettier flower
just a little further on.
And so she ran farther and farther from the path.
The wolf, however,
went straight to Grandmother's house
and knocked at the door.

"Who is outside?" asked Grandmother.

"It is Little Red-Cap," said the wolf.
"I have brought you cake and milk.
 Open the door."

"Just lift the latch," Grandmother called.
"I am too weak to get up."

The wolf lifted the latch, and the door flew open.
The wolf walked in
and went straight to Grandmother's bed,
and then, in one gulp, he swallowed her.

Then the wolf put on her spectacles
and her nightcap,
climbed into the bed,
and pulled the blankets up to his chin.

Little Red-Cap had been running about
looking for flowers,
and now she had more than she could carry.
So again she set out
on the path to Grandmother's house.

When she arrived,
she was surprised to find the door wide open,
and as she stepped into the room,
she thought, "My Goodness,
how frightened I feel!
And usually I like so much
to come to Grandmother's."
She walked over to the bed
and there was Grandmother
in her spectacles and nightcap,
looking very strange.

"Oh, Grandmother, what big ears you have," said Little Red-Cap.

"The better to hear you with, my dear."

"And Grandmother, what big eyes you have."

"The better to see you with, my dear."

"And Grandmother, what big hands you have."

"The better to hold you with, my dear."

"But Grandmother, what a dreadfully big mouth you have!"

"THE BETTER TO EAT YOU WITH, MY DEAR."

And with that,
the wolf jumped up out of the bed,
and swallowed poor Little Red-Cap in one gulp.

"That was a fine dinner!" said the wolf,
and he climbed back into the bed.
He soon fell asleep,
and began to snore very loudly.

A hunter was passing by and thought,
"How that old woman can snore!
I had better look in and see if she is all right."

So he went inside, and over to the bed
and there lay the wolf, the very same one
that he had been hunting for so long!

The hunter was about to fire his gun.
Suddenly he thought,
"Surely, the wolf has swallowed
the old grandmother.
Perhaps she might still be saved.
I shall not shoot."

So he found a pair of scissors,
and began to cut open the stomach
of the sleeping wolf.
He had made only a few snips,
when he saw the red cap.
He cut a little more,
and out jumped the little girl.

111

"Oh, how frightened I was!" she cried.
"How dark it was inside the wolf!"

In another moment
Grandmother came out, weak and shaky.
Then Little Red-Cap ran
to get great, heavy rocks,
with which they filled the wolf's belly.

The wolf awakened and jumped up to run away,
but the weight of the rocks was too much for him.
He fell over backwards, and died.

And now they were very happy.
The hunter took the wolf's skin
and went on his way.
Grandmother ate the cake and drank the milk
that Little Red-Cap had brought,
and soon she felt much better.
And as for Little Red-Cap, she thought:
"Never again, for the rest of my life,
shall I leave the path and run into the forest
when my mother forbids it."

Out in the Rain

Group 1:   Willie Duck and Wallie Duck,
Played in an April shower,
Without any rubbers on
For almost an hour.

Group 2:   Neither had a raincoat
And neither had a hat,
But their mother didn't worry
Or fret about that.

Group 1:   Of course their mother saw them,
But she didn't scold.

Group 2:   She didn't even tell them
That they'd both catch cold.

Groups
1 and 2:   Willie Duck and Wallie Duck
Were wet clear through.

Teacher: And what about their mother?

All: She was out there too!

by Leland B. Jacobs
picture by Ed Renfro

Joey
Kangaroo

Do you know where baby kangaroos live?
They live in their mother's "pocket."
All baby kangaroos
are called joeys.
The mother kangaroo
carries her joey with her,
in her pocket.

by Patricia K. Miller and Iran L. Seligman
pictures by Ed Renfro

A baby kangaroo is only one inch long
when it is born.
It has no fur.
It cannot see.
As soon as it is born it crawls into the pocket.
The baby kangaroo stays in the pocket
for four months.
The pocket keeps it safe and warm.
The mother makes milk in her body
to feed the joey.
If you could look in the pocket,
you would see how much bigger
the joey is growing.

In and out!
In and out!
Now the joey
can leave the pocket.
He comes out
to jump and play.
His mother shows him
how to eat grass.
Then he goes back
into the pocket.

As the days go by,
the joey grows bigger
and bigger.
One day he tries
to get into the pocket,
but he is too big now.
His mother will not
let him get in.

Now the joey takes care of himself.
He finds grass to eat.
He jumps along with his mother.

Kangaroos live together in small groups.
A group of kangaroos is called a mob.
The strongest male kangaroo is the leader
of the mob. He had to fight the other male kangaroos
to become the leader. He had to show
that he was the strongest kangaroo. He had to show
that he could take care of the mob.

Kangaroos sleep during the day.
At night they move about, looking for food.

126

Kangaroos eat grass.

They nibble leaves from small trees.

They eat fruit and vines.

Kangaroos have long, heavy tails.
They rest on their tails when they sit.
They push with their tails when they jump.
They push down with their tails
. . . and up they go!
Look how high a kangaroo can jump!
Joey kangaroo is growing.
One day soon he may be the leader of his mob.

MONDAY'S CHILD

an old rhyme adapted
with pictures by Sonia O. Lisker
handlettering by Linda Yakel

Monday's child is fair of face,

Tuesday's child is full of grace,

Wednesday's child is full of woe,

Thursday's child has far to go,

Friday's child is loving and giving,

Saturday's child works hard for a living,

Sunday's child is quick to remember,

the season's not lost,
there's always September.

How many miles to Old Norfolk
To see a magician breathe fire & smoke?
   One, two, three, four,
   Only three miles more.
How many miles to Christmas Cove
To eat of an applecake baked with clove?
   One, two, three, four,
   Only two miles more.

How many miles to Newburyport
For trinkets & sweets of every sort?
  One, two, three, four,
  Only one mile more.
How many miles to Lavender Spring
To hear a fine trumpeter play for the King?
  One, two, three, four,
  Here we are, we'll go no more.

a rhyme by Clyde Watson
pictures by Wendy Watson

139

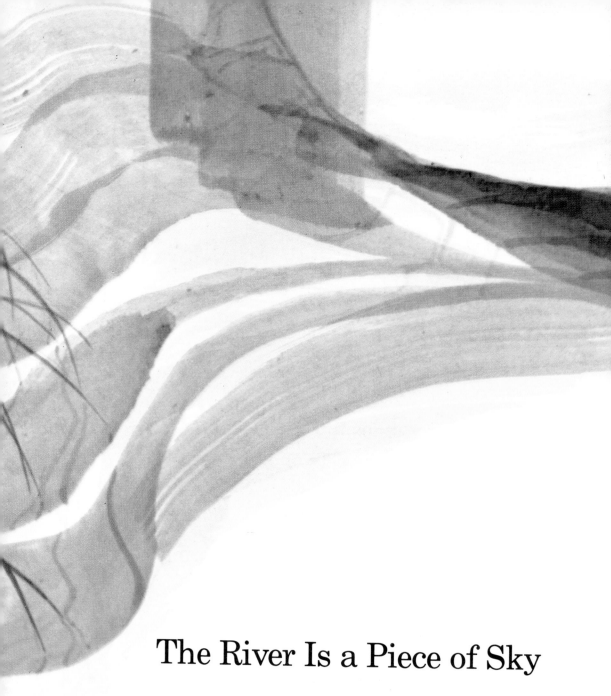

The River Is a Piece of Sky

by John Ciardi, picture by Ed Young

From the top of a bridge
The river below
Is a piece of sky—
   Until you throw
   A penny in
   Or a cockleshell
   Or a pebble or two
   Or a bicycle bell
   Or a cobblestone
   Or a fat man's cane—
And then you can see
It's a river again.

The difference you'll see
When you drop your penny:
The river has splashes.
The sky hasn't any.

Knots on a Counting Rope

by Bill Martin Jr
pictures by Joe Smith

"Grandfather, tell me the story again.
Tell me who I am."

"I have told you many times, Boy."

"But tell me again, Grandfather.
Tell me about my name."

143

"You know your name, Boy.
   You know the story by heart."

"But it sounds better when you tell it.
   Please tell it over and over, Grandfather.
   I like to hear you say my name."

"Then listen carefully, Boy.
This may be the last time for telling the story.
The counting rope is almost filled with knots."

"This cannot be the last time, Grandfather.
Promise that this will not be the last time."

145

"I cannot promise you anything, Boy.
I love you. I love you very much.
That is better than a promise."

"And I love you, Grandfather.
Tell me the story again. Please."

"Once there was a boy child. . . ."

"I was the boy child, wasn't I, Grandfather?"

"Yes, you were the boy child in the story."

"And I was very strong, wasn't I, Grandfather?"

"No, you were not strong, Boy.
You were very little and very sick.
We thought you were going to die."

"But *you* knew that I wouldn't die, Grandfather.
Tell me that part again."

"One day when you were very sick
and your breath was too weak for crying,
two great blue horses came galloping by.
Suddenly they turned and looked at you.
You reached up your arms to them."

"And that is when you named me!"

"Yes, we named you Boy Strength-of-Blue-Horses.
  It is a strong name."

"Did I need a strong name, Grandfather?"

"All children need strong names to grow strong."

"And what did you say, Grandfather?"

"I said, 'See how the horses speak to him.
  They are his brothers
  from beyond the dark mountain.
  This boy child will not die.
  The blue horses have given him strength to live.'"

"Did I grow strong, Grandfather?"

"Yes, Boy, you grew strong
  and you are becoming stronger every day.
  Some day you will be strong enough
  to cross over beyond the dark mountains."

"How strong must I be, Grandfather?
   Tell me that part again."

"You must be so strong, Boy,
   that you will not speak with anger
   even when your heart is filled with anger."

"And that is not all, Grandfather.
  Tell me the next part."

"You must be so strong, Boy,
  that you want to know
  what other people are thinking
  even when you are listening
  to your own thoughts."

"Now tell me the last part, Grandfather."

"You must be so strong, Boy,
  that you will stop to think
  of what happened yesterday
  and what will happen tomorrow
  in knowing what you want to do today."

"Is it hard to be strong like you, Grandfather?"

"Strong people are not born strong, Boy.
 They become strong by thinking they are strong.
 They dream of themselves as being strong enough
 to cross over the dark mountains."

"Will I ever be strong enough
 to cross over the dark mountains, Grandfather?"

"You already have crossed over
some of the dark mountains, Boy.
The mountains have no beginning and no ending.
They are all around us.
We only know that we are crossing them
when we want to be weak
but choose to be strong."

"Maybe I will not be strong enough, Grandfather,
to cross over all of the dark mountains."

"Oh, yes, you will be, Boy Strength-of-Blue-Horses."

"Then you must keep telling me the story,
Grandfather.
You must never stop telling me the story."

"But I will stop telling the story, Boy,
when I have tied the last knot
on the counting rope.
Now that I have told the story again,
I tie another knot, just as I did before.
When the rope is filled with knots,
you will start telling the story to yourself.
That is the way you know you are strong.
That is the way you become strong."

Jenny the Juvenile Juggler

by Dennis Lee

pictures by Peter Lippman

Jenny had hoops
    she could sling in the air

And she brought them along
    to the Summerhill Fair

And a man
    from a carnival sideshow
      was there,

handlettering by Ray Barber

And it's

> Oops! Jenny, whoops! Jenny,
> Swing along your hoops, Jenny,
> Spin a little pattern as you go;

Because it's

> Oops! Jenny's hoops! Jenny,
> Sling a loop-the-loop, Jenny,
> Whoops!
> Jenny, oops!
> Jenny, O!

Well, the man was astonished at how the hoops flew,
And he said, "It's amazing what some kids can do!"

Act number one
GOLDIE
and the bears

and
now at the carnival,
Act Number Two is
Jenny

the Juvenile Juggler.

And it's "Oops! Jenny,"
whoops! Jenny,

Swing along your hoops, Jenny,

Spin a little pattern
as you go;

Because it's Oops! Jenny's hoops! Jenny!

Sling a loop-the-loop, Jenny,

WHOOPS!

Jenny, oops!

Jenny, O!

The Tiger,
The Brâhman,
and the Jackal

a folktale of India
pictures by Mamoru Funai

Once upon a time
a tiger was caught in a trap.
He tried in vain to get out through the bars,
and rolled and bit with rage and grief
when he failed.

By chance a poor Brâhman came by.

"Let me out of this cage, O pious one!"
  cried the tiger.

"Nay, my friend,"
  replied the Brâhman mildly,
"you would probably eat me
  if I did."

"Not at all!"
  swore the tiger with many oaths.
"On the contrary,
  I would be forever grateful,
  and serve you as a slave!"

Now when the tiger
  sobbed and sighed and wept and swore,
  the pious Brâhman's heart softened,
  and at last he consented
  to open the door of the cage.

Out
$p_op_{pe}{}^d$
the tiger,
and seizing
the poor man,
cried,

"What a fool you are!
   What is to prevent my eating you now,
   for after being cooped up so long
   I am just terribly hungry!"

In vain the Brâhman pleaded for his life;
   the most he could gain
      was a promise to abide by the decision
         of the first three things
            he chose to question
               as to the justice of
                  the tiger's action.

So the Brâhman first asked the *pípal* tree
what it thought of the matter,
but the *pípal* tree replied coldly,
"What have you to complain about?
Don't I give shade and shelter
to every one who passes by,
and don't they in turn
tear down my branches to feed their cattle?
Don't whimper—be a man!"

Then the Brâhman, sad at heart,
   went farther afield
      till he saw a buffalo turning a well-wheel;
         but he fared no better from it,
            for it answered,
            "You are a fool to expect gratitude!
               Look at me! While I gave milk
         they fed me on cotton-seed and oil-cake,
            but now I am dry, they yoke me here,
               and give me refuse as fodder!"

The Brâhman, still more sad,
asked the road to give him its opinion.

"My dear sir," said the road,
"how foolish you are to expect anything else!
Here am I, useful to everybody,
yet all, rich and poor, great and small,
trample on me as they go past,
giving me nothing
but the ashes of their pipes,
and the husks of their grains!"

On this
the Brâhman turned back sorrowfully,
and on the way he met a jackal,
who called out,

"Why, what's the matter, Mr. Brâhman?
You look as miserable
as a fish out of water!"

Then the Brâhman told him
all that had occurred.

"How very confusing!"
said the jackal,
when the recital was ended.
"Would you mind telling me all over again,
for everything seems so mixed up!"

The Brâhman told it all over again,
but the jackal shook his head
in a distracted sort of way,
and still could not understand.

"It's very odd," said he sadly,
"but it all seems to go in at one ear
and out at the other!
I will go to the place where it all happened,
and then perhaps I shall be able to give judgment."

So they returned to the cage,
by which the tiger was waiting for the Brâhman,
and sharpening his teeth and claws.

"You've been away a long time!"
 growled the savage beast.
"But now let us begin our dinner."

"Our dinner!" thought the wretched Brâhman,
 as his knees knocked together with fright.
"What a remarkably delicate way of putting it."

"Give me five minutes, my lord!" he pleaded,
"in order that I may explain matters
 to the jackal here,
 who is somewhat slow in his wits."

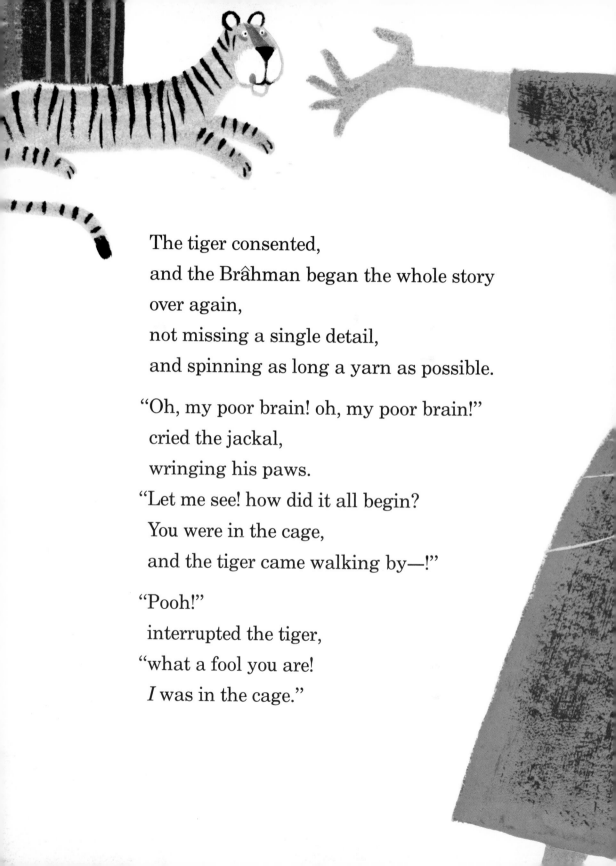

The tiger consented,
and the Brâhman began the whole story
over again,
not missing a single detail,
and spinning as long a yarn as possible.

"Oh, my poor brain! oh, my poor brain!"
cried the jackal,
wringing his paws.
"Let me see! how did it all begin?
You were in the cage,
and the tiger came walking by—!"

"Pooh!"
interrupted the tiger,
"what a fool you are!
I was in the cage."

"Of course!" cried the jackal,
  pretending to tremble with fright.
"Yes, I was in the cage—
  no, I wasn't—
  dear! dear! where are my wits?
  Let me see—
  the tiger was in the Brâhman,
  and the cage came walking by—
  no, that's not it either!
  Well, don't mind me,
  but begin your dinner,
  for I shall never understand!"

"Yes, you shall!"
returned the tiger,
in a rage at the jackal's stupidity.
"I'll make you understand!
Look here—I am the tiger—"
"Yes, my lord!"
"And that is the Brâhman—"
"Yes, my lord!"
"And that is the cage—"
"Yes, my lord!"
"And I was in the cage—
do you understand?"

"Yes,—no—Please, my lord—"

"Well?" cried the tiger, impatiently.

"Please, my lord!—how did you get in?"

"How!—why in the usual way, of course!"

"Oh dear me!—

my head

is beginning

to whirl

again!

Please

don't be angry,

my lord,

but what is

the usual way?"

At this the tiger lost patience,
  and, jumping into the cage, cried,
"This way!
  Now do you understand how it was?"

"Perfectly!" grinned the jackal,
  as he dexterously shut the door.
"And if you will permit me to say so,
  I think matters will remain
  as they were!"

Keep a Poem in Your Pocket

Keep a poem in your pocket
and a picture in your head
and you'll never feel lonely
at night when you're in bed.

The little poem will sing to you,
the little picture bring to you
a dozen dreams to dance to you
at night when you're in bed.

by Beatrice Schenk de Regniers
drawing by Charles Brey